Inteligro Math

The Holistic Approach to Math and Science for the Next Millennium

Tiffany Rhoades Earl

About Inteligro Math

"I just love it when the 'lights turn on' in the eyes of my math and science students. As a pilot teacher of Inteligro Math I'm privileged to see this often.

Inteligro Math is a unique and refreshing approach to what many consider to be desert-dry drudgery – learning math. It fleshes out and gives life to the suddenly fascinating foundations of mathematics.

Inteligro Math explains the why. It provides insights into the thinking of great men and women who have passionately pursued the truth, and as a consequence benefited humankind by furthering the sciences. It delves into the reasons they were driven to invent new branches of mathematics. Most importantly, it inspires students and mentors alike, to think, create, and invent in the same way.

Most of us have no problem studying things that we're interested in. Inteligro Math makes math and science interesting."

–Karl Black, Inteligro Math teacher, New Commonwealth School, Boise, Idaho

"As a homeschooling mother who endured the pain and tears (both theirs and mine) that accompany the teaching of traditional mathematics to children, I knew there had to be a better way. This book confirms what my instincts told me: there is a better way. Inteligro Math enlarged my understanding of the scope of math and science and helped me comprehend that all of us do far more mathematical thinking than we realize. Much of the fear and frustration that typically surround the teaching of mathematics can be removed when these concepts and ideas are implemented in your education."

–Christine Elkington, homeschooling mother, Tooele, Utah

Inteligro Math

The Holistic Approach to Math and Science For the Next Millennium

Tiffany Rhoades Earl

Leadership Education Mentoring Institute Press
Bountiful, Utah

Inquiries regarding requests to reprint all or part of this book, or distribution or publishing questions, should be addressed to:

Leadership Education Mentoring Institute Press
Lemiinstitute.com or tiffany@lemiinstitute.com
Printed in the United States of America.

Contents

Acknowledgments

I would like to acknowledge the following without whom I could not have written Inteligro Math:

1. My Husband, Richard Earl, who embodies the Characteristics of a Scientist.
2. The Math seminar at George Wythe College, "Teaching Math Through the Classics" presented by Dr. Oliver DeMille, for teaching me the language of Math.
3. Dr. Troy Henke, for his liberal arts high school curriculum, which gave me a clear idea of where our young scholars are headed.
4. Aneladee Milne, for her Scholar Systems and her invaluable partnership in every endeavor we do at LEMI *(Leadership Education Mentoring Institute)*, including the creation of The Pyramid Project™.
5. Our mentors at Lemi who teach Inteligro Math.
6. My Heavenly Creator, to whom I give all credit and acknowledgement, and without whom I am nothing.
7. Kim Simmerman who made the writing of this book possible.

Thank you, each of you, the parents and teachers who dedicate so much time and effort teaching our children!

Sincerely,

Tiffany Rhoades Earl

Introduction

I paused a moment as I watched my husband lean in closer to the plastic incubator. He held the plastic tank of triops up to the light.

"What are you doing?" I asked.

He wrote something in his little red notebook and finally answered me.

"Counting."

"Counting what?"

"I'm counting how many triops hatched, and how many are still alive."

"How many hatched in that batch?" I said.

"Twelve hatched. It is five days later and now there are two."

"What does that mean?" I asked.

"It either means my tank is too small, there's not enough food, or these triops are cannibals."

"Hmf." I said as I walked past him. There were two hundred tanks of triops sitting on the tables. He was jotting down data from each one. And I was observing first hand, the life of a scientist.

Science is incredibly fun, incredibly exciting, and can also be incredibly tedious and laborious. So why do it?

Inteligro Math is not only about the "why" but also about the "what" and "how".

"Inteligro" is a derivative of the Latin words "intelligo" meaning "intelligence, light, truth, and understanding"- and the word "integro" meaning "whole". Thus Inteligro Math is the holistic approach to understanding Math and Science. It covers the "why", "how", and "what".

Just as the base of a pyramid has four cornerstones, so does Inteligro Math. The four cornerstones explain why we need math and science, how to do math and science, and just exactly what math and science is.

Mathematicians and scientists:

1. Work to discover Truth – the first cornerstone
2. Can take their ideas and experiments to a clear end, using Logic – the second cornerstone.
3. Have certain habits in common whether they study behavioral sci

ence, earth science, medical science, or even political science, etc. And these habits and characteristics can be developed – the third cornerstone.

4. Convey their measurements and computations to the world through the language of math, using Newtonian Math – the fourth cornerstone.

Inteligro Math is desperately needed in our schools and in our homes. Staggering data stares us in the face. Approximately 90 percent of American patents used to go to Americans. The number has now dropped to 51 percent. Why? Because math and science have been separated from each other and because they are seldom done from the perspective explained in this book.

By applying Inteligro Math in our schools and in our homes, math and science will come alive and thrive once again.

The scientific method, used for hundreds of years, is the old way of doing Science. Welcome to the Inteligro Method™, the approach to science that will propel us into the next millennium.

Chapter One
TRUTH

"That darn donkey! He keeps lying down in the water every time he crosses the river!" Thales' workers couldn't solve the problem. The donkeys were taken to the salt mine, loaded down with salt, and then led down and up the path to drop it off. It was hard work for the donkeys, as the salt was heavy. The donkeys were expensive, and to lose one because he'd lie down in the path was frustrating. Beating the donkey didn't work. Coaxing the donkey didn't work.

Finally, Thales was consulted. He watched what was happening. He figured out what the real problem was and came up with what he thought would be a good solution. They tried it, and it worked. Instead of loading the donkey with salt, Thales had the donkey loaded with dry sponges. At first the donkey's load was light. When the donkey got to the river, he lay down in the water just as he usually did. After several minutes he stood back up. He then had to walk up the next hill heavily laden with dripping sponges.

After a few days of this the donkey quit lying down in the water. Once again salt was placed on his back, but he still didn't lie down in the water. Thales had discovered what the donkey had discovered. When the donkey was laden with salt and submersed himself in the water the salt dissolved, making the second half of his trip much lighter. (Wouldn't you lie down in the river, too?) But when the sponges filled with water the load was exceedingly heavy for the second half of the trip. Smart donkey.

The primary purpose of math and science is to discover truth. This deep yearning for truth is vital to understanding why mathematicians and scientists go to such great lengths for discovery. Finding and describing truth is the end and purpose of math. Without truth, math is empty—just meaningless numbers. Searching for truth and understanding can lead to the betterment of mankind.

Why do we care about truth? Because we are happier when we align our lives with natural law. Man's purpose in life is to have joy. Searching out natural laws and aligning our lives with these laws allows this to happen.

That there are natural laws is indisputable. What are "natural laws"? They are the laws that continue to exist no matter what man does to legislate them away. Even if twenty legislatures at the federal level pass a law stating that apples will no longer fall off trees, it doesn't change the truth: apples fall off trees. If one township passes a law that adultery will no longer tear families apart, it doesn't change the truth: adultery leads to unhappiness because families lose trust, which is the basic building block of long-lasting relationships, and causes families to fall apart.

The purpose of math and science is to find truth—truth in all subjects. There are a myriad of scientific disciplines: earth sciences, physics, chemistry, political science (the science of government), biology, mechanics, engineering and many, many more. There are hundreds of ways to dissect this earthly experience and look at specific parts to discover what is true. But no matter what the discipline, no matter what the category, no matter what the particular problem is that needs solving, the goal is the same: to discover what is true.

Thales wanted to change the donkey's behavior. He had to know the truth about why the donkey lay down, how salt reacted in water, how sponges reacted in water, and whether the donkey could learn something new. Only by knowing these natural laws could he apply them and get the results he desired.

If you examine documents written by moral mathematicians or scientists, you will find they have something in common. No matter what the topic of study, they share one common goal:

to discover truth. If discovering truth is the aim and purpose of math and science, it then becomes apparent that we need a measuring stick for truth. What is to be used?

C.S. Lewis employed four methods for finding truth. Inteligro Math uses all four of these ways, (reason, historical evidence, personal experience, and faith/revelation). All men have faith, for faith derived to its simplest form is belief—and then action following that belief. All men believe *something*. One man might believe in God, while another man believes you can't know if there is a God. Yet another believes there isn't a God. Any way you slice it, all of them have faith. All believe something.

A man's belief can be traced to written documents (or oral stories for civilizations without writing). In America before 1960, these written documents were the Bible and The Declaration of Independence. [i]

What book, or books, do you measure all truth by? The book(s) you name is your *core* book. What is your core book? Even if you believe there is no right and no wrong, you have some core writing to trace your belief to. Find it. For those who follow the traditional American core book, that book is the Bible.

In order to do Inteligro Math, you need to know your core book.

Take a moment and write your fundamental beliefs and where you find them, or in other words, write the name of your core book: ____

____

____

____

This exercise is extremely important. You cannot do Inteligro Math without it. Don't go on until you've written the name of your core book, the book or writing against which you measure all truth.

I have one teacher whose core book is The Declaration of Independence. Many of my other teachers' core book is the Bible. Hitler's was *Mein Kamf*. For some it is The Torah, for some The Koran. I have a friend whose core book includes *The Biography of a Yogi*.

What is yours? Write it down.

Good. You are ready to learn the two skills that go along with the first Inteligro, "Truth": learning by study and by faith.

If math and science are all about truth, then we must have something by which to measure that truth. There are two truth-measurers: that which is self-evident, and that which is revealed. Your core book holds what you believe to be revealed and self-evident truths. Use it as a measuring stick. Study it.

If math and science is about discovering what is true, then the first math and science book you should master is your core book–the book you believe to be truer than any other book.

I encourage my students to spend a minimum of thirty minutes a day studying their core book, annotating it mathematically. This may be new to some of you. For the sake of learning this important scholar skill, let's assume for a moment that the Book of Genesis, found in the Bible, is part of your core book.

Let's study the first several verses together–annotating it mathematically–looking for truth, equations and insights. Since this is the book we measure all truth against, and this is the book we believe holds truth, and because math and science is all about truth, let's take the pains to study it right.

(If your core book is The Koran or the Naghamadi, after you go through this exercise in Genesis you can turn around and do the same thing in your own core book.)

The first step in this study is to realize that we have a basic assumption: we already believe our core book to be true. The purpose of our core studies right now is not to decide whether it is still true, but rather to discover the truth within it.

If you are adverse to brain pain, you might want to stop right now. Document studies hurt. It's hard work and can be frustrating. I promise you, though, that it is extremely rewarding if you stick with it. If you aren't willing to follow the next couple of pages of studying a document with me, don't expect your friends and students to do it either. But if you are willing, you will set the example for nations to follow. For in this case, one is equal to infinity.

There are four things we need in order to start:

1. The document
2. Pen
3. Paper
4. A dictionary

I especially like to use Webster's 1828 *American Dictionary of the English Language*; it is available online if you don't have a copy. Language is an extension of our feelings and thoughts, and vice-versa, language generates feelings and thoughts. The definitions found in this particular dictionary lead man to have inspired thoughts and feelings. I also like to have a mathematical dictionary close at hand. Remember, we are studying this document from a math and science viewpoint. We are looking for truth, equations and insights. Here we go.

As I open my book the title reads:

THE FIRST BOOK OF MOSES
CALLED
GENESIS

Stop right there! What has been said so far? *The first book. Hmmm, first implies that there is more than one.* Are you following my thoughts? What do we know about the books of Moses? There are five books, called the Pentateuch. If you didn't know that, you can look it up. Let's go on.

Moses, I know who he is. He was the chosen deliverer of Israel. He was a type and a shadow of the Messiah. He lived...etc., etc., etc. Make the words stick. Don't just read them, study them! What do you know about Moses? Who was he? We know that this chapter is about the creation of the earth. That means Moses must have had this revealed to him. Let's go on.

CALLED GENESIS. Why "Genesis"? Did Moses name it Genesis or was that name added later? What does "Genesis" mean? Let's look it up in the *Bible* dictionary and then in Webster's 1828 dictionary.

There are several publications of the Bible; feel free to look up what your Bible dictionary says. Mine says (among other things) that genesis is a Greek word meaning "origin or beginning" and that the book of Genesis gives the account of many beginnings.

All right, let's look up Genesis in Webster now. It says:

> "1. The first book of the sacred scriptures of the Old Testament, containing the history of the creation, of the apostasy of man, of the deluge, and of the first patriarchs, to the death of Joseph. In the original Hebrew, this book has no title; the present title was prefixed to it by those who translated it into Greek.
>
> 2. In geometry, the formation of a line, plane or solid, by the motion or flux of a point, line or surface."

Oooh. This is really cool! Did you notice that genesis is a math word? In geometry, genesis means the formation of a line, plane or solid. It is made by the motion or flux of a point, line or surface. It involves action or maybe a catalyst of some sort. Motion and flux is involved. This might be important to my understanding of the text.

At this point I either write in my text (yes, I write in my Bible) or I annotate on paper. This definition is worth noting. Next to the word Genesis I write, "formation caused by motion or flux." I write something to remind me of the meaning I just looked up; perhaps I write the entire definition in my notes.

So far we have spent anywhere from five to fifteen minutes studying in our core book, and we are barely past the title. Quantity isn't our goal today, quality is. This is what it means to study in our core book for thirty minutes a day. Let's go on.

Remember, there are several versions of the Bible. Here is the text in the one I have in front of me:

Chapter 1

"In the beginning God created the heaven and the earth."

Stop. What was said? On my paper I write, "God created both the heaven and the earth." Does anything stand out to you? Do you want to look something up? If so, go ahead, this is your study. Perhaps you want to look up the word "created."

Next verse:

> "And the earth was without form, and void; and darkness was upon the face of the deep. And the Spirit of God moved upon the face of the waters."

I already have at least six questions. How about you? Mine were, *"Does form mean some sort of physical pattern? What is meant by void? Does that mean a nothingness and emptiness? Was the earth just a whole bunch of material without recognizable patterns–kind of like a glob of clay? What does Moses mean by 'darkness upon the face of the deep?' What is THE DEEP? And where did the waters come from? Are the waters part of the material? What happens when the Spirit of God moves upon the waters? I'd better keep reading and find out.*

"And God said, Let there be light; and there was light."

Stop right there. There's an equation right in front of us. Here's what I see: when God speaks, action follows. Or in other words, God's spoken word equals action or equals light. I also see: God equals light.

In my notes I write:

"God's spoken word = action. Action = light. God's word = light." In other words, "a = b, b = c, and a = c." Does that remind you of anything?

What do you see?

When I find equations I write them in my Inteligro portfolio on the equations page. I'll talk more about the portfolio later, it is a great companion to this book and for those applying the principles of Inteligro Math.

Some of you might disagree with my mathematics and my logic. You may be right; I'm still learning. That's the point. I'm learning.

Let's keep going.

> "And God saw the light, that it was good: and God di-

vided the light from the darkness."

I immediately see two things in this verse. One is the math word "divided" and the other is an equation. Equations imply balance. Imagine a balance scale if you would. If it is set properly the two sides hold items and measure weight—the equality or inequality of the items.

I like to bring a balance scale with me to class when I teach my students how to study their core books. The students love taking turns putting weights on the two sides of the scale and trying to equalize the balance. This manipulative makes the idea of "equations" come to life. They can easily grasp the idea of one side being congruent to, or equaling, the other side. Playing with physical manipulatives to create equations helps our minds grasp the equations we read in our core books. I suggest you try it, even if you don't have a balance scale. You can use apples to make equations, you can use pencils, or whatever—just do a kinesthetic activity to cement the idea of equations in your brain.

What equation did I see in verse four? Light was good. "Was" is a form of the "be" verb: am, is, are, was, and were. "Is" in math can mean "equals." Therefore, "Light equals good. Or light = good."

How many times throughout your core book is "light" referred to? Did you know that optics, the study of light, is a major branch of mathematics? I can learn a lot about the science of optics, and studying my core book is a great place to start. I've personally started keeping a log of the science I find about light from my core book, and it is amazing what science I'm learning; it's really fun, too. Some of my favorites are:

- Where there is light, there can be no darkness.
- Keep your eye single to the glory of God.
- The Glory of God is intelligence, in other words, light and truth.

Okay, I just went off on a tangent. Watch out—that's what happens when you start studying math and science in your core book. You start making connections, having "a-has" and some times, like an electron heated up, you start jumping up and down.

I like finding the "if this...then this..." statements or equations. These jump out at me. You need to watch out, though, because once you start studying your core book for truth, math, science and equations you'll start seeing them everywhere.

I was reading Tzu SSu's *The Way of the Mean* and began annotating it like a scientist as well. Just look at the equations and "a-has" I had:

Equations:

- Man of true breeding = mean in action
- Man of no breeding = reverse
- True breeding = consistently holds to the mean
- Man of no breeding = no sense of moral caution
- Perfect = mean in action
- Therefore, man of true breeding = mean in action = perfect
- Traps: learned run to excess; ignorant fall short

All of these came from the first three paragraphs. Tzu SSu, who lived about 300 B.C., was a grandson of Confucius and enjoyed philosophy.

The point is: learning to think like this helps us in all our studies, and searching in our core books for truth makes sense. I think you get the picture. The purpose of math and science is to discover truth (natural law—those immutable laws) and to master and use it by aligning oneself with it. The best place to start studying math and science is in our core books. Our core book is that set of books against which we measure all truth. As we find natural law and align ourselves with it, we can find happiness and joy—the purpose of life.

Thus, the first cornerstone of Inteligro Math is Truth. A pyramid has four cornerstones upon which it is built, just as math and science do. The next cornerstone is Logic.

Chapter 2
LOGIC

An apple is a fruit. A fruit is an orange. Therefore an apple is an orange, correct?

Our ability to reason, to follow a line of logic, to see connections and non-connections, makes us human beings—incredible, infinitely perfectible human beings.

Logos (logic) and pathos (emotion) are intricate parts of man, and both are essential to being scientists. I'll discuss the heart—the pathos—in Chapter 3, for now we'll discuss logos.

How we think, our ability to define and solve problems is essential to coming to truth. Logic is the ability to reason something out, to see the end from the beginning. Webster's dictionary defines logic as, among other things:

- The art of thinking and reasoning justly
- The art of using reason well in our inquiries after truth, and the communication of it to others
- The purpose of logic is to direct the intellectual powers in the investigation of truth and in the communication of it to others

The second Inteligro is "Logic." In order to come to truth we must be able to reason. Since truth is our goal, and the obtaining of it and aligning our lives to it the means of joy, it stands to reason that *we need to learn to reason.*

Having said this, let us discuss how we can develop our reasoning abilities.

Let me suggest three ways:

1. Learn to follow a line of logic.

This takes work. We do it when we read, we do it when we think about something long enough, and we do it when we solve problems. Increase the difficulty of your reading venue. My three favorite authors for increasing my logic skills and reasoning abilities are Shakespeare, Tolstoy, and C.S. Lewis. Who is your favorite? Whose line of reasoning do you love reading? If you don't know, then read more.

Einstein used his mind to think through problems in a theoretical manner, following a line of logic. He asked the right questions, and by applying his knowledge and ability to reason he deduced what should be the right answers.

According to Lynn and Gray Poole, "For nearly fifty years thousands of scientists have taken his deductions, experimented with them in a physical manner. Continuously they have found that he was correct and did lead science toward totally new interpretations."[ii]

We too, can learn to think through problems in a theoretical manner, figuring problems out, and solving mysteries.

2. Play a musical instrument.

One of the characteristics of a scientist is the ability to see patterns and use organizational strategies. We will go into this in detail in the next chapter, but it bears mentioning here. Playing a musical instrument requires the association, recognition and command of patterns. Not only does playing an instrument well require both sides of the brain, but it also develops reasoning because of the patterns involved.

I'm not kidding when I challenge you to play a musical instrument. Six months ago three of my children and I started piano lessons. What's uncanny is that they can memorize the songs about 100 times faster and easier than I can. We are all beginners, but my 12-year-old son listens to me practice my songs, and when I'm not at the piano he'll sit down and play my songs! I walked over to him once and noticed that he didn't even have the music in front of him. What I'm saying is you're not too old to learn an instrument, but if a child begins musical instruction between the ages of eight and twelve they learn at a faster rate.

I'm excited that my children will be developing synapses in their brains through playing music. Einstein was a violinist, and even he knew it attributed to his ability to do math.

3. Don't close your eyes to the obvious.

Sometimes our social mores blind us to the truth all around us. If we close our eyes to evidences that surround us, we literally aren't using all of our senses. When Thales' donkey fell in the water it was obvious what was happening. He was lightening his load. Why couldn't the workers see that? Why could Thales? It was because he didn't close his eyes to the evidence. When the donkey got back up its burden was lighter.

That information gave the solution: do something so that when the donkey lays down in the water, and then gets back up, his burden is heavier–thus, the sponges.

These three ways to increase one's ability to reason can be done with just a little bit of effort added to our day. Many of us already read, so read on a higher level–get out of your comfort zone. Many of us listen to music, so start *playing* music. Even fifteen minutes a day can increase our brain's abilities.

We all have senses with which to take in the evidences all around us. When Solomon ordered the child cut in two, he never expected to kill the child. He used the obvious: a mother's love. When Petruchio wanted to communicate with Kate, he did the obvious: spoke her language. When Screwtape's atheist began questioning his unbelief in a God, Screwtape got him busily concerned with the mundane orders of life–like eating–not thinking.

There are several things I teach my students to do that help them develop the use of logic. In Chapter 1 we talked about finding equations, and this takes reasoning skills. Also, when my students do their Newtonian Math (discussed in detail in Chapter 4), I expect them not only to master the way being taught, but also to figure out another way to solve the same problems. This takes a lot of effort.

Of course, you can do as the sophists do and use logic to steer someone away from truth. This, of course, isn't the goal of Inteligro Math. In Greece and Rome many men studied under the sophists. Sophists used reasoning and logic that was sound in appearance only. "These men have obscured and confounded the nature of things by their false principles and wretched sophistry."[iii]

Being able to follow a line of logic is essential in even maintaining our liberty. I read a book recently that was hailed by some of my peers as "liberating," "wonderful," a "great read." It was even quoted in churches. My interest was piqued, so I bought the book and consumed its content.

I was disgusted and abhorred. It had the flavor of Freud. Those of you who have read Freud you will understand my meaning. The author told these beautiful, wonderful stories that made sense and tugged at the heartstrings; and then, being trained in logic, rhetoric and sophistry, she gave a conclusion that, to the untrained eye, seemed completely obvious and correct. One trained in logic or in following a line of logic would notice the red flags. The conclusions had nothing to do with the stories and evidences; they were simply policies this politician wanted to see adopted in America. Having learned to see the unseen, I understood what the author was really saying.

We must learn to think and to reason, to use logic and to deduce it. A person who can't follow an action to its clear ends is easily led and is often full of blame and rationalization. When Hitler invaded Austria without a single shot being fired, very few Austrians opened their eyes to obvious truths: Hitler had strangled the economy in the first place and wasn't the one to credit for its rebounding. Hitler had taken their freedoms in one fell swoop. Austrians were no longer allowed to fly their flag, sing their anthem or give their greetings to God or to each other, but instead had to honor The Man (Heil Hitler). They were no longer allowed to have any opinion that differed from the Third Reich's.

All of this didn't seem to matter to them at first because their economy had rebounded.

Any amount of logic in this situation raises a red flag. A small amount of reasoning urged families like the Von Traps, to do as the Von Trapps did, which was to see things as they really were.

The father said to his children, "If we want to keep our lands and our money, our home and our friends, our jobs and our schools, we must give up our faith in God. There are no two ways about it. If we want to keep our freedom, our honor, and our lives, we must leave our beloved Austria."[iv] Now that's logic—sound logic.

The highest ability of reason and logic is to see life as it really is, as it really was, and as it really will be. This is the way to happiness and liberty. Inteligro Math involves using this reasoning ability. The ability to reason is vital—to see things as they really are—in order to come to truth.

Not only do scientists use reason, they also have several other abilities and habits. Once I began studying the lives of scientists and mathematicians, I found a pattern. They all had several things in common. These commonalities are called "The Habits of a Scientist." This is the third Inteligro and the subject of the next chapter.

Chapter 3
THE HaBITS OF A SCIENTIST

It must have been frustrating to want to be one thing and to have his father pressuring him to be another. Galileo sat in the cathedral staring at the ceiling. He didn't stare too long when his eye noticed the movement of the chandeliers. I wonder how long he stared at them before he noticed the pattern. It wasn't long after noticing the pattern that he ran home and tested his ideas.

Lister knew the truth all too well. Surgery was a person's last choice. They were as likely to die from infection due to the operation as they were to die from the original problem. It was 1821, and Lister was concerned.

Harvey knew that blood flowed in an orderly way, the same way for each person. "What was that way?" he wondered.

Patterns. They are everywhere and in everything. They are ordinary. They are mundane. They are the fabric of our lives. They can also be illusive, hidden, confusing, and hard to grasp.

No matter what they are, patterns are the key to unlocking droves of knowledge. Scientists know this. Any scientist or mathematician who has changed the world has the uncanny habit of seeing patterns everywhere and in everything.

The first vital habit of a scientist is to notice patterns.

Habit 1: Notice Patterns

The habits scientists naturally have can be developed. We can develop them, and so can our children. I challenged my students to come to class each week and share the patterns they noticed. We did this for twelve weeks, and now my students can't stop seeing patterns.

One of my students noticed this pattern: if she wanted her mom to say "yes" to something, all she had to do was rub her fingers through her mom's hair, giving her a head massage before asking her question. Her two sisters, unbeknownst to her, did the same thing!

Some of my students noticed architectural patterns in their homes, and some noticed the patterns of human nature in the classics they were reading. One boy noticed that the emperors in Rome died mostly of suicide or murder. Some patterns were as simple as noticing social mores and customs, like everyone wearing matching socks to school. Whatever the pattern was, it wasn't mocked or made light of.

The pattern Galileo noticed–the way the chandelier was swinging and gently rolling back and forth in the cathedral–could seem a small thing, but it led to huge medical breakthroughs.

The high number of deaths due to infection after surgery disturbed Lister. Everybody had noticed the pattern, but he did something about it.

Harvey's breakthrough on the study of the heart launched our understanding of the human body!

In our classroom, no pattern was too small or too common to just throw out. It wasn't long before the students had developed the habit of seeing patterns. One girl noticed Fibonacci's numbers in nature and didn't even know who Fibonacci was or how important her discovery was.

I have a friend who is a scientist. He studies slides of the tissues of dead animals in order to find out the cause of death. There are very few people in the country whose eyes can see what his can see. It is all about "pattern recognition." In fact, there are no books written on what he knows. He is a leader in his field, and he knows what he knows because of experience. When he starts to see abnormalities in the normal patterns on the slide, he can discern the cause of death or mutation. In order to define the cause of problems, our eyes must be trained to see patterns. We can define problems when we can see patterns.

The founders of America, the men and women who helped frame the forms that still impact us today, were scientists. Statesmen are scientists of governance and of human nature. They are men and women who study forms (patterns) and implement forms in all aspects of life in order to promote a quality life. The challenge of political scientists is, according to Ronald Reagan, "...to have the vision to dream of a better, safer world and the courage, persistence and patience to turn the dream into reality."

A careful study of classics can train our minds to see patterns. The beauty of the classics is that they reveal patterns in human nature as well as the advantages and disadvantages of whatever pattern the author is discussing. A careful study of any classic reveals the inherent strengths and weaknesses, pros and cons, or natural laws surrounding specific forms and patterns.

Recently a study on education was reported on C-Span. The study took three levels of chess players and set up a test to divine the intelligence of the three groups. The lower level chess players looked at a chessboard with a grouping of chess pieces. The pieces were then removed and the players were asked to replace the pieces in their exact positions on the board. They were able to correctly replace only four pieces.

The second level chess players were given the same assignment. Eight pieces were replaced correctly.

The third level chess players were then tested. These master chess players were able to replace sixteen pieces correctly.

The test was then altered a bit and repeated. This time the chess pieces were placed randomly on the board instead of in recognizable chess patterns.

All of the groups were able to replace only four pieces correctly.

What did this mean?

It means that the way intelligence had previously been measured and the way it seems it should be measured is now being articulated. Intelligence used to be measured by memory. What the chess study showed is that it isn't memory that makes the difference; it is pattern recognition and organizational strategies.

The advanced chess players were able to replace sixteen chess pieces because they recognized more patterns, they knew more patterns and they understood more patterns. They intrinsically had more choices to make when playing chess because of knowing these patterns. They could also easily recognize these patterns and duplicate them.

When the chess pieces were placed randomly on the board there was no pattern recognition—there was just plain memory; and memory paled in comparison to pattern recognition.

Thinking is connecting the dots. It's seeing patterns. Forms and systems are recognized only as we learn to see patterns. Scientists notice patterns.

Habit 2: I Wonder

I am married to a scientist, an inventor. He's not happy unless he's inventing a new way of doing something, no matter what his occupation is. He has owned various businesses over the years where "real science" was involved. It was by living with a person who exhibits these characteristics and habits and by studying the lives of various scientists that I noticed some vital habits they all had in common.

What is exciting is that all of these habits can be learned and developed. The second habit is to wonder. Scientists have a natural sense of curiosity.

Lavoisier knew that human and animal life depended on something taken into the lungs. He wondered what that something was and how it acted.

Galen's "I wonders" included: What are the parts of the body? How do they function? What are the tissues and muscles that cover the skeleton of bones?

Vesalius wondered about the form and structure of living

things.

Harvey's wonderings centered on the movement of the blood through the body.

Newton wondered what white light was made of.

Lister was appalled by the high death rate caused by infection and wondered how to stop people from dying due to infection.

Hippocrates wondered if all disease was supernatural or if some was caused by earthly means.

Marie Curie wondered why pitch blend weighed more after it was burned than before.

What did each of these men or women contribute because of their natural curiosity?

Lavoisier (1743-1794) became the father of modern chemistry. He drew up a Table of elements, which is still used today.

Galen (130-200) published his scientific experiments in anatomy, which served the medical field for over 1,300 years.

Vesalius published his scientific experiments in anatomy, propelling man's understanding of the human body into current thought.

In 1628, Harvey discovered that blood circulates in the body. It does not flow from liver to heart to brain in the circuitous route Galen proposed. Harvey charted the exact course of the blood.

Newton gave us incredible laws in physics and in the science of optics, among many other things.

Lister discovered a way to kill infection-causing germs.

Hippocrates proved that many diseases were caused by earthly means and gave doctors their current diagnostic guide.

Marie Curie and her husband discovered radium.

What do you wonder about? What are your wonderments?

I heard my children singing a child's song the other day that went like this, "What do you think...when there's nothing to think about? What do you do, when there's nothing to do? What you think about, think about, think about, is what's really you."

What do you think about? What are your wonderments?

There is a page in the Inteligro Portfolio dedicated to tracking the patterns you notice, and another one for writing down what you wonder about. Use the Portfolio to track the patterns you see and the questions you have.

When my son was six he said to me, "Mom, I wonder if heaven is as good as food." I smiled broadly and held back a chuckle because that is sooo Joseph. He loves good food. He must associate heaven with something good.

Children are full of natural curiosity and wondering–from why the sky is blue, to why eggs change from a liquid to solid when cooked, to a myriad of other ideas. Their wonderings are often deep and poignant, and if we adults would slow down our lives a little we would hear our natural curiosities as well.

My nine-year-old daughter wonders why we don't just invite our close friends and families to move with us to an island. That way, she reasons, we could live in peace and happiness. She is only nine and is building her own utopia, asking the most deeply profound questions that philosophers have asked since time began: how can people live in peace and happiness one with another?

Once again–and this is not rhetorical–what do you wonder about? Jot down some of your thoughts, and if you have the Inteligro Portfolio, jot them down in there on the "I Wonder" record.

____

____

____

____

____

____

Habit 3: Challenge Assumptions

Because scientists notice patterns, and patterns often disprove some of society's most basic assumptions, they have learned to challenge assumptions.

Hippocrates challenged the assumption that all disease was supernatural, caused by the angry or happy Gods.

Vesalius challenged Galen's assumption that human body systems were identical to those of the Barbary apes.

Even Galen knew the importance of challenging assumptions and learning from personal experience. He insisted that his students dissect Barbary apes themselves, not just rely on his findings.

Harvey challenged Vesalius's assumption about the way blood flowed because his anatomical research showed otherwise.

Pasteur challenged the assumption that disease was born of nothing.

The American colonists challenged the English system of the divine right of kings.

Scientists don't challenge any and all assumptions; they challenge assumptions that don't match the patterns they've observed. But one thing they can do is notice when something is an assumption. Can you?

When you are reading a book, can you pick out the author's most basic assumptions? This is a very important skill. Have you noticed my most basic assumptions as I write to you? Think about them for a minute, and then I'll tell you what they are.

I assume that there is a right and a wrong. I assume there are eternal, indisputable truths. I assume you want to be happy. I assume a good many other things as well.

Notice assumptions when you read. This will also help you know if a line of logic will come to a conclusion you agree with. Everything has to start with an assumption.

When evidences and patterns are contrary to an assumption, scientists have the habit of challenging them.

I challenge one of Darwin's primary assumptions, and since it is one of his primary assumptions, I have to follow his line of logic carefully because it may mean that I disagree with his conclusions.

I challenge his assumption that "animals reproduce in much greater numbers than can possibly be supported by the environment in which they live, and more than is necessary to maintain the species."[V]

Why do I challenge this assumption? In part, because evidence shows otherwise. When countries have encouraged population control limits, whether by law or by social pressure, those civilizations have crumbled (i.e., Rome, Greece and Egypt). Encouragement of race propagation grows a nation and civilization. That is just one area of discrepancy that I have noticed. There are more.

Are there established "assumptions" for which you have found evidence to the contrary? What do you do when you see discrepancies? Do you encourage your children and students to ignore discrepancies, as most people have done throughout history, or do you encourage your children and students to follow their hunches and reasoning to their clear ends?

In 1798 when Jenner wanted his findings on smallpox published, members of the Royal Society of London resounded a loud "No!" They were appalled when he published it himself using his own funds.

When news got out that Copernicus could prove that the sun, not the earth, was the center of the universe and that the planets orbited around the sun, he was almost burned as a heretic and kept his discoveries silent until his friend published them for him when Copernicus was on his death bed.

Was Vesalius applauded when he published his experiments and findings that the human body was drastically different from Barbary apes? Absolutely not. For thirteen hundred years, Galen's writings were considered "The Bible" on human anatomy.

Many frown upon the practice of challenging assumptions. Not true scientists, though; they encourage it when the evidence shows discrepancies.

Habit 4: Ask the Right Question

Isaac Newton said that asking the right question would "unravel the secrets from a mass of information and could pinpoint an answer of scientific value." He's right. Can you go through masses of information and find the pertinent? Not all questions and data are equal.

"I wonders" and asking the right question go hand-in-hand. Einstein was sixteen when he became curious about the speed of light and asked the right question: "If you could be on the front of a wave of light moving through space, would you have the feeling of being in motion?" "No," was his answer because motion was relative. To the person at the front of the light wave, it would seem that he or she was in the same place or stationary.

We have already listed several scientists' right questions in the "I Wonder" habit. For now, suffice it to say that asking the right question is the crux of effective science. I will go into this further in Chapter 5 when I discuss the Inteligro Method™.

Habit 5: The Heart

Having the heart of a scientist is half the battle when it comes to doing science. Being willing to try things over and over and changing something here and there takes heart and dedication.

Doing something because you care creates a different output than doing something because you are paid to do it or have to do it. Mercenaries–hired soldiers–never fight as well as soldiers who are protecting their homelands, their wives, their children and their rights.

Lavoisier, the father of modern chemistry, cared about many things and applied his knowledge to many areas in his life. He realized that the grain output from each section of his farm directly related to the amount of manure in that section. He ended up calculating exactly how many head of cattle should roam each field. By herd management and crop rotation, he doubled his grain yield.

His farm wasn't all he cared about. He experimented with tax reform, widespread school literacy projects, production and distribution of gunpowder and conducted studies in combustion, to name a few.[vi]

When we care about the little things–the projects our children, spouses, students and friends are engrossed in–it really matters. Caring is important. What things do you care about? What things do you care about enough to do something about?

In 200 A.D., the Romans revered the human body as a descendant of the Gods. That is why Galen could not dissect human bodies. So he found the closest thing to it: a tailless species of apes, the Barbary apes.

In the 1500s, it was still illegal to dissect human bodies, but that didn't stop Vesalius. He cared so much about finding out what was true and real about the human body that he went to great lengths to do so. He didn't resort to murder, but he did resort to theft. The first body he dissected was found during the night hanging from a tree. Later he found a corpse on a hill.

He compared Galen's notes on the Barbary apes to what he found in the human corpse. He took copious notes and dissected the bodies using tools he made himself.

I don't necessarily recommend doing what Vesalius did, but the curiosity of a scientist is not just mental. It reaches the heart. Wanting to know the truth breaks the rules of convention, sometimes surpasses social norms, and pushes the scientist past mediocre limits. Scientists who contribute to the happiness and welfare of mankind don't give up in the face of adversity.

The question is: what things do you care about deeply enough to learn the truth surrounding them?

Habit 6: Embrace Failure

How many times was Colonel Sanders rejected before he sold his chicken? Almost a thousand! How many times did you unsuccessfully ride your bike before you could do it without thinking? How many times did you cook macaroni and cheese before you found the way you love it? How many names did you go through before you finally chose your first child's name?

Scientists don't look at failure as a big, fat "F". They look at it as new knowledge, and new knowledge is valuable. Scientists look at failure as part of the process of discovering truth, and they trust the process.

Scientists experiment. When an incongruence is noticed between the patterns observed and society's assumptions, scientists set up tests to find out what is true, whether it is the true nature of a cell, an element, human behavior, the stars, the function of water, or how carbon reacts with oxygen.

Children are not afraid of failure until they experience other people's disappointment. Every time my five year old slips up, whether falling off a counter, tripping in the hall or calling someone by the wrong name, she comes back with an incredibly indomitable spirit: "Good that I didn't break my neck, huh?" or "Good that I only skinned my knee, huh?" and "It's good that I know your real name now, huh?"

This is the same attitude scientists have. Failure just brings us one step closer to finding the truth. Scientists know that failure is part of the process of discovery. By studying the other greats, they themselves come to embrace "the process," not fear it.

Galen proved his predecessors wrong on some points, Vesalius proved Galen wrong on some points and Harvey proved Vesalius wrong on some points. Each also applauded his predecessors' breakthroughs and contributions to knowledge, and each wasn't afraid to show discrepancies between what people thought was true and what now could be proven otherwise.

A scientist welcomes new proofs, even if it proves their own theory wrong. Why? Because science is about discovering what is true, and any deviation from this isn't real science–it is men in power who don't want a shift in that power.

Habit 7: Read Original Works

Scientists stand on the shoulders of those who came before. Harvey read Copernicus, Galen, Aristotle, Hippocrates and Vesalius. Newton read Copernican theories, the writings of Galileo, the complete works of Johannes Kepler and the detailed published works on the science of optics.

Inteligro Math teaches students to study original works and writings by other scientists. In public schools the skills to do this often aren't taught until law school. Instead, students learn by rote rather than discovery.

I have found that students who are fourteen years old and even younger can learn these skills. In the Pyramid Project™, the Inteligro Math Scholar Project I created for the young scholar, we do "document studies," through which the student gains practice and skills by studying the original works of mathematicians and scientists who have made a difference in the world. Some of these readings include John Tyndall, Archimedes, Laotse, Tzu Ssu, Thales, Darwin, Julien Offray de Lamettrie, Kant, Soren Kierkegaard, and more.

We mimic the core book study process. We read on a scholarly level, figuring out what the author is saying, following their line of logic, and annotating their assumptions, equations and proofs. Then we ask if we have any evidence that coincides with what is taught or contradicts what is taught. It's rather exciting. During the colloquia after the original documents are studied our ideas, "a-has" and connections are literally bouncing off the walls!

Reading original works not only teaches the students to know and understand what the author understood, to follow a line of logic, to think deeply and to keep the fire of natural curiosity burning, it also mentors the students in the process of discovering truth and in how to think.

Note: If you are interested in having Tiffany Earl present a seminar in your area about Inteligro Math, which includes training you in document studies, contact her at tiffany@lemiinstitute.com.

Habit 8: Whole Not Specialized

Scientists learn everything they can. In 1842, Dr. Long read about the properties of ether and nitrous oxide and performed the first surgery using an aesthetic.

It is in the crossing of two seemingly unrelated subjects that breakthroughs occur. It is when life is looked at as a whole that connections can be made.

In the book, *The New Commonwealth School*, Aneladee Milne and I explain the damage that specialization does to us. Milne tells how Booker T. Washington spent his life trying to teach black Americans not to be specialized. She says, "Specialization is inherent to slavery. Slavery is dependent upon specialization because it is the best way to maintain maximum control. If each part of the machine does its job it needn't do or know anything else."

Most slaves were highly specialized laborers. Milne says, "We learn through this experience in our history that the institution of slavery was an institution of highly specialized workers."

Scientists see the world holistically, not in meaningless parts segregated from the whole. When Lister was appalled by the high death rate caused by infection he read two seemingly different articles. One was Louis Pasteur's theory that microorganisms suspended in air cause fermentation and putrefaction. The other was a scientific article about carbolic acid.

These two things combined made a connection with what Lister was already wondering about. He didn't think that contact with pure air caused infection, but that microorganisms–germs–settled on wounds and caused the fermentation or infection.

He began to see a clear path to the answers to his questions: "how can infection be stopped once it has begun and how can wounds be treated to kill the germs?" He used cobalt to "sterilize" surgical equipment before performing surgery. He saw the results he wanted, did some further testing and soon learned how to help patients survive surgery in a time when many died due to infection even though the original ailment was removed.

Lavoisier, the father of modern chemistry combined business, farming, agriculture, human behavior, law, government production of gun powder, literacy in schools, taxes and much more, and gave France and others tax reform, public schools, more productive farms, the Periodic Table of the Elements, understanding of combustion and much more.

Inteligro Math encourages scientists to "go deep" in more than one field, and to constantly be learning. This is where breakthroughs occur and where valuable, meaningful contributions are made.

Habit 9: Judging

Making judgments is part of science. As mentioned before, C.S. Lewis learned to use the following in order to compare and contrast one thing to another:

- Reason
- Historical evidence
- Personal experience
- Revelation

His first encounter with one of his best liberal arts mentors, Professor Kirk, went like this (watch how Kirk teaches young C.S. Lewis to reason and to judge):

> "You are now," said Kirk, "proceeding along the principal artery between
> Great and Little Bookham."
> I stole a glance at him....I began to "make conversation" in the deplorable manner which I had acquired...I said I was surprised at the "scenery" of Surrey; it was much "wilder" than I had expected.
>
> "Stop!" shouted Kirk with a suddenness that made me jump. "What do you mean by wildness and what grounds had you for not expecting it?"
>
> I replied I don't know what, still "making conversation." As answer after answer was torn to shreds it at last dawned upon me that he really wanted to know. He was not making conversation, nor joking, nor snubbing me; he wanted to know. I was stung into attempting a real answer. A few passes sufficed to show that I had no clear and distinct idea corresponding to the word "wildness,"

and that, in so far as I had any idea at all, "wildness" was a singularly inept word. "Do you not see, then," concluded the Great Knock, "that your remark was meaningless?" I prepared to sulk a little, assuming that the subject would now be dropped. Never was I more mistaken in my life. Having analyzed my terms, Kirk was proceeding to deal with my proposition as a whole. On what had I based (but he pronounced it baized) my expectations about the Flora and Geology of Surrey? Was it maps, or photographs, or books? I could produce none. It had, heaven help me, never occurred to me that what I called my thoughts needed to be "baized" on anything. Kirk once more drew a conclusion-without the slightest sign of emotion, but equally without the slightest concession to what I thought good manners: "Do you now see, then, that you had no right to have any opinion whatever on the subject?"

By this time our acquaintance had lasted about three and a half minutes; but the tone set by this first conversation was preserved without a single break during all the years I spent at Bookham....

The idea that human beings should exercise their vocal organs for any purpose except that of communicating or discovering truth was to him preposterous. The most casual remark was taken as a summons to disputation. I soon came to know the differing values of his three openings. The loud cry of "Stop!" was flung in to arrest a torrent of verbiage which could not be endured a moment longer; not because it fretted his patience (he never thought of that) but because it was waiting time, darkening counsel. The hastier and quieter "Excuse!" ushered in a correction or distinction merely parenthetical and betokened that, thus set right, your remark might still, without absurdity, be allowed to reach completion. The most encouraging of all was, "I hear you." This meant that your remark was significant and only required refuta-

> tion; it had risen to the dignity of error. Refutation (when we got so far) always followed the same lines. Had I read this? Had I studied that? Had I any statistical evidence? Had I any evidence in my own experience? And so to the almost inevitable conclusion, "Do you not see than that you had no right, etc."
>
> Some boys would not have liked it; to me it was red beef and strong beer.[vii]

Through this type of mentoring, C.S. Lewis began to discipline his mind. He learned how to think. He describes several popular philosophies of his day—neoplatonics, materialism, atheism, agnosticism and Christianity—that he learned to compare and contrast. He then spent his life promoting the form he fell in love with and which he believed brought human happiness and explained human suffering.

Abraham Lincoln also studied relentlessly his whole life, disciplining his mind to judge wisely. He could think so clearly by the time Douglas came along that he didn't get caught up in the wrong argument. It wasn't only states' rights he was arguing about; it was about right and wrong. It wasn't a government and national form he was debating; to him the argument was cultural. The argument was about values and morals, which manifested themselves nationally and in government.

C. S. Lewis was a scientist of human nature, Abraham Lincoln of government. What are you a scientist of? Can you compare and contrast the evidences and myriad of data in order to come to conclusions about the world around you?

These are the vital habits of a scientist that can be developed by young and old alike. Once our students are seeking after truth, using their minds to follow a line of logic and living like a scientist, it is essential that they have the ability to communicate their findings to others. This is our next chapter, Newtonian Math.

Chaper 4
NEWTONIAN MATH

"Ten, twenty, thirty, forty, fifty, sixty, seventy, eighty, ninety, one hundred. We can count by tens, up to one hundred, we can count by tens. Ready, here we go: ten, twenty, thirty, forty, fifty, sixty, seventy, eighty, ninety, one hundred." My five year old learned this song when she was three.

Isn't Newtonian math wonderful? **It is how we measure and compute both quantity and quality.** It is the language of mathematics. It is the language of science.

Truth exists whether we have the language for it or not. Isaac Newton invented calculus simply so he could figure out something and have the language to identify, qualify and quantify it.

Simply put, Newtonian math is the language we use to express the measurement of our math and science.

Sadly, in some schools it is the *only* cornerstone of math that is taught; and with any one of the four Inteligros missing, the math just isn't whole. Without the understanding that math is about truth, what does measurement matter? Without the ability and drive to understand the world around us, what good does the measurement do?

Have you ever been the one in a math class to raise your hand and say, "why?" Newtonian math without the "why" is a bunch of formulas that are memorized and plugged in but not understood. So what if a right answer comes up because the right formula was used? If the student doesn't know why he or she used it and can't create a formula on her own to solve a new kind of problem in the future, what good did the math do?

That's the way many students feel. I have friends who feel so liberated when they come to realize that there are four Inteligros, not just one. There are four cornerstones on a pyramid that make the foundation strong and sound.

Newtonian math—the math you and I know all about but may not have completely understood—is essential. It is how we communicate the truths we find. It is our mathematical language.

When Newton pondered about why and how planets were held in exact orbits (which, it is true, came about in part when the apple hit him on the head), he discovered his "inverse square law of gravitation." This law states that any two bodies in the universe attract each other with a force directly proportional to the product of their masses and inversely proportional to the square of the distance between them. [viii]

He didn't want this law to be just theoretical; he wanted to prove it, measure it. There was no math precise enough to work out his proof. What did he do? He worked and worked and worked and created a language and measuring tools precise enough to do it: calculus. Newton devised integral and differential calculus and applied them to proving how and why celestial bodies move as they do.

Newtonian math simply refers to the language of math; it is how we express the measurements, the data, the qualities and quantities found.

But Inteligro Math doesn't just do Newtonian math the way you and I learned it in public school. At best, that method creates puppets; at worst, it creates math-haters.

Children in Asia score higher in mathematics than children in America. According to Joan A. Cotter, cutting edge math curriculum developer and trainer of teachers across America, it is because of the difference of culture. She says, "A child learns how to count correctly in Korea, whereas in America a child's counting is usually by rote."[ix]

Even Albert Einstein knew that learning by rote rather than pattern recognition was counterproductive. He was considered a poor student because he disliked "having to learn and to memorize routine facts that he would be required to write by rote on examination papers."[x]

According to Cotter, the way mathematics is taught in most public schools is changing, and with poor results. According to international studies such as TIMSS and PISA, the U.S. scores low compared to other countries. In 2004, of the 1.2 million students who took the ACT test, only 40 percent were deemed ready to study college algebra. Twenty-five percent of college students take remedial math. And, as I said, only 51 percent of patents go to U.S. citizens, down from 90 percent.

What we want is mathematicians and scientists who are on the cutting edge in physics, biology, mechanics, engineering and government. Yes, in all the disciplines. We want scientists who can discover and communicate truth.

There are three things I teach my students as they study Newtonian Math:

1. Take responsibility for your education.

Nobody educates you but you. You are the one who decides whether or not to learn. You cannot blame a bad teacher, a mom or a stupid textbook for you being a blockhead—or a genius.[xv] The truth is you are all geniuses , so believe in yourself, take responsibility for your choice to learn or not to learn and choose to learn!

2. Develop the scholar skills necessary to read math classics.

One of the habits mentioned in the previous chapter is the reading of original works. I can't say enough about this habit, though it does take practice and skill. There is no better practice for studying math and science classics than the daily reading in your core book. Original math and science classics are written in paragraph form, like most people's core books, not just in numbers and math signs.

Actual math and science classics are the best place to go for developing even Newtonian skills. For it is in these pages that the purpose for the algorithms, which are simply procedures, are laid out. In step three I'll explain more about algorithms, or procedures, and the way Inteligro Math takes them to a higher level of thinking when studying them, right now I want to explain something about math and science classics.

Because many of us didn't study math classics in our formal schooling days, but mostly studied math and science textbooks, it might seem a bit daunting to pull out a mathematician or scientist and read him or her.

I've pulled several math and science classics off my bookshelf and want to give you a taste, just a paragraph or two from a few of them, so that you can see that Albert Einstein, Henri Poincare', Louis Agassiz, and Archimedes are approachable–by us and by our children.

Hopefully the first paragraph or two of each will wet your appetite and make you want to read more of them, if you haven't already.

In *Evolution and Permanence of Type*, an essay by Louis Agassiz, contemporary of Darwin, Agassiz refutes the Darwinian Theory of Evolution. It is a very appetizing essay. He begins,

> In connection with modern views of science we hear so much of evolution and evolutionists that it is worth our while to ask if there is any such process as evolution in nature. Unquestionably, yes. But all that is actually known of this process we owe to the great embryologists of our century, Dollinger and his pupils K.E. von Baer, Pander, and others, –the men in short who have founded the science of Embryology. It is true there are younger

men who have done since, and are doing now noble work in this field of research; but the glory must, after all, be given to those who opened the way in which more recent students are pressing forward.

The pioneers in the science of Embryology, by a series of investigations which will challenge admiration as long as patience and accuracy of research are valued, have proved that all living beings produce eggs, and that these eggs contain a yolk-substance out of which new beings, identical with their parents, are evolved by a succession of gradual changes. These successive stages of growth constitute evolution, as understood by embryologists, and within these limits all naturalists who know anything of Zoology may be said to be evolutionists. The law of evolution, however, so far as its working is understood, is a law controlling development and keeping types within appointed cycles of growth, which revolve forever upon themselves, returning at appointed intervals to the same starting-point and repeating through a succession of phases the same course. These cycles have never been known to oscillate or to pass into each other; indeed, the only structural differences known between individuals of the same stock are monstrosities or peculiarities pertaining to sex, and the latter are abiding and permanent as type itself. Taken together the relations of sex constitute one of the most obscure and wonderful features of the whole organic world, all the more impressive for its universality.[xi]

Agassiz uses his reasoning abilities to talk right to us. This is real science. This is the way scientists write about their discoveries. Our students and our children can read Agassiz, and after figuring out what he is saying, by annotating his lines of logic, figuring out his assumptions, and writing down his "if this...then this" equations, our students can ask, "Is he right?" And "Is this true?" In other words, "Do I agree with Agassiz? With his line of logic? With his proofs and with his assumptions? And with his conclusions?" And believe it or not, its a completely exhiliarating exercise.

Let's look at Albert Einstein. In his book *Relativity*, the first two paragraphs of chapter three, titled "Space and Time in Classical Mechanics" goes like this:

> The purpose of mechanics is to describe how bodies change their position in space with "time." I should load my conscience with grave sins against the sacred spirit of lucidity were I to formulate the aims of mechanics in this way, without serious reflection and detailed explanations. Let us proceed to disclose these sins.
>
> It is not clear what is to be understood here by "position" and "space." I stand at the window of a railway carriage which is traveling uniformly, and drop a stone on the embankment, without throwing it. Then, disregarding the influence of the air resistance, I see the stone descend in a straight line. A pedestrian who observes the misdeed from the footpath notices that the stone falls to the earth in a parabolic curve. I now ask: Do the "positions" traversed the stone lie "in reality" on a straight line or on a parabola? Moreover, what is meant here by motion "in space"?....[xii]

Something remarkable happens when we read the very words of a mathematician or scientist. That is, there is a "transfer of soul". When you read the two paragraphs of Einstein, did you not begin to get a feel for the remarkable man? Did you start to see how his mind differed from yours or mine, and where there were similarities? Do your children ever ask questions like his? Mine do. Do you ever ask questions like him?

I love reading Einstein because then I get a feel for him, for what he thought about, and how he thought. When a child learns to speak, are they not mimicking those around them? Why would it hold any different for thinking? We want to learn to think, to reason, to see things to their true ends. Why would it not stand to reason that we learn to think in the same way we learn to speak–by mimicking others.

We can mimic how Einstein thought only if we know how and what he thought. We can learn to reason as he did only if we follow his lines of reason. The more we expose ourselves to the thinking of mathematicians and scientists, the more we learn to think like mathematicians and scientists.

So let's read two more. In his book, *Science and Method*, Henri Poincare', the man hailed as mathematical universalist and one of the greatest mathematicians since Gauss, discusses the basic methodology and psychology of scientific discovery. The first two paragraphs of chapter one, The Selection of Facts, are below:

> Tolstoi explains somewhere in his writings why, in his opinion, "Science for Science's sake" is an absurd conception. We cannot know all the facts, since they are practically infinite in number. We must make a selection; and that being so, can this selection be governed by the mere caprice of our curiosity? Is it not better to be guided by utility, by our practical, and more especially our moral, necessities? Have we not some better occupation than counting the number of lady-birds in existence on this planet?

> It is clear that for him the word utility has not the meaning assigned to it by business men, and, after them, by the greater number of our contemporaries. He cares but little for the industrial applications of science, for the marvels of electricity or of automobilism, which he regards rather as hindrances to moral progress. For him the useful is exclusively what is capable of making men better.

I can't stop there. I must give you one more paragraph so that you might know where Poincare' is going to take us:

> It is hardly necessary for me to state that, for my part, I could not be satisfied with either of these ideals. I have no liking either for a greedy and narrow plutocracy, or for a virtuous unaspiring democracy, solely occupied in turning the other cheek, in which we should find good people devoid of curiosity, who, avoiding all excesses, would not die of any disease–save boredom. But it is all a matter of taste, and that is not the point I wish to discuss.[xiii]

Oh, I must stop there though it is another two or three paragraphs before Poincare' finally finishes telling us his stand.

These and others like them are the classics I encourage you to consume to help you learn the language of math and science. Just one more taster.

In *The Sand Reckoner*, Archimedes says:

> There are some, king Gelon, who think that the number of the sand is infinite in multitude; and I mean by the sand not only that which exists about Syracuse and the rest of Sicily but also that which is found in every region whether inhabited or uninhabited. Again there are some who, without regarding it as infinite, yet think that no number has been named which is great enough to exceed its multitude. And it is clear that they who hold this view, if they imagined a mass made up of sand in other respects as large as the mass of the earth, including in it all the seas and the hollows of the earth filled up to a height equal to that of the highest of the mountains, would be many times further still from recognizing that any number could be expressed which exceeded the multitude of the sand so taken. But I will try to show you by means of geometrical proofs, which you will be able to follow, that, of the numbers named by me and given in the work which I sent to Zeuxippus, some exceed not only the number of the mass of sand equal in magnitude to the earth filled up in the way described, but also that of a mass equal in magnitude to

the universe.....[xiv]

It is by reading the mathematician or scientist that we learn to think like mathematicians and scientists. This is by far the best way to study Newtonian Math. But there is one more way which is also helpful.

3. Take your math text lessen to the next level, exponentially!

Math texts, as opposed to math classics, require a different skill. You must read the actual algorithm, or way of doing that problem. An algorithm is simply a procedure. Learn to read math and science texts and master the procedures taught in them.

Math textbooks are synopsis of math procedures. They are "parts" of math and science taken from the "whole" picture. Algorithms, or procedures for measuring, computing, and communicating about math are an important part of math. Students can learn to read math textbooks and grow their skills in Newtonian math. This is not the only place a person can develop their Newtonian skills, nor is it the best place when left on its own.

Textbook lessons are a great way to study procedure, but math classics give the whole picture.

Inteligro Math has a unique approach to math and science textbooks. After understanding and mastering the procedure that is taught in a particular lesson, figure out another way–a different procedure or another algorithm–to do the same thing. It is this easy: at our house we wash the dishes by rinsing them off and putting them in the dishwasher. My friend doesn't have a dishwasher; she washes hers by hand. Either way, the dishes get clean.

Taking math to the next level is like realizing there is more than one way to wash a dish. If you have a column of numbers you are adding together, Saxon Math teaches a certain procedure for adding them. It says to take the numbers that add to ten, cross them out, and then add the tens and the leftovers. Is that the way you learned it? It wasn't until I was 25 years old and saw that my friend could add a column of 30 numbers four times faster than me and with fewer mistakes that I realized there might be a better way. I asked her to teach me, and she did. It was so cool! Now I add my columns this other way.

I count by fives. Any number, five or greater, has a five in it. Six has five in it with one left over; seven has five in it with two left over; nine has five in it with four left over. First, I go down the column and count by fives. Then I go down the column and, touching the number in the right spots, add the leftovers plus any numbers under five. Seven has two left over, and if you look at the numeral "7" you can see two spots: the place you start to write it and the place you end writing it. The number "8" has three leftovers, and you can see three horizontal lines on the "8" that I touch with the pencil as I count. You can see the trick. Anyway, it is just another way of adding up a column. If this makes sense to you, go ahead and try adding the following column:

9 9 9
7 7 7
5 5 5
4 4 4
3 3 3
7 7 7
6 6 6
8 8 8
9 9 9
2 2 2
1 1 1

7 7 7

I wrote it three times so that you can try, on your own, to come up with a third way of adding a column of numbers. Don't not do it. Try it! It's harder than you think. It exponentially increases the amount of work you are doing, but it also forces you to think.

My students who take the challenge to come up with new procedures have a blast and at the same time are developing a keen sense of logic, fortitude, stick-to-itiveness and creativity. They are our next generation of scientists and mathematicians. Instead of getting into trouble for coming up with another way to solve the problem, they are applauded.

Coming up with alternative algorithms is a key element to the Newtonian Inteligro.

For hundreds of years science has been practiced using many different methods. Read on to find the new technology, which will propel us into the next millennia of science.

Chapter 5
THE INTELIGRO METHOD™

"Kathy, I'm telling you we don't have enough money right now." I sighed as I listened to my dad talking to my mom; I quietly shut the door to their room. Mom and Dad never argued in front of us eight kids. In fact, I used to think they never argued. Nevertheless, somehow I intrinsically felt their financial struggles and burdens.

I walked down the hall to my room wondering why I couldn't buy new jeans, why we kept having to downsize when our family kept growing, why our car kept breaking down and why my mom was stressed.

Sound familiar? How many of you have had similar dilemmas? Maybe not with finances, but perhaps with a health problem, with a particular relationship you care deeply about or maybe with your work.

Even at fifteen I used the Inteligro Method™, though I didn't know that's what I was doing. You will probably find that when you successfully solve something you use this method, too.

I went to my room, and that night as I studied in my core book I decided to do a "topical" research instead of chronological. I went to the index and looked up words such as: money, wealth, finance, prosperity, happiness and so on. I began looking up the references.

Two hours later I'd made up my mind. I knew there were eternal truths, eternal laws. I knew inside of me that when I did as my Creator asked, following His laws, He was bound to do His part. I had seen over and over that He was only bound when we did what He asked.[xvi]

It was very much like picking up a stick–when one end is picked up, the other end follows. That's how I saw it. I wanted to know the parameters of the "prosperity" stick. I wanted to prosper. I wanted my family to prosper. I was tired of the pain I was feeling, the pain my mom and dad were feeling and our lack of freedom.

The following Sunday night at Family Council, I announced my intention. I wasn't very diplomatic at fifteen. "Mom, Dad, I've decided I'm not eating out on the Sabbath any more." They looked at me a little perplexed. We had the tradition of eating at a restaurant occasionally on Sundays. My dad worked out of town during the week, and it was a nice family treat to go out to dinner at a buffet. It just happened to fall on Sundays.

"I've decided that I won't be breaking the Lord's Day any more. We are promised great blessings if we keep His day holy, and I want those blessings, which include:

- a fullness of the earth
- the herb
- good things, whether for food or raiment, or houses, or barns, or orchards, or gardens or vineyards
- things to please the eye and gladden the heart; for taste, for smell to strengthen the body and to enliven the soul." [xvii]

My mom and dad knew I was serious. I then explained what I knew inside. If we could just find God's laws, the natural laws regarding prosperity, then we could get out of the fix we were in. If we would just repent from whatever laws we were breaking, apply the atonement and change our course, we wouldn't stay in the cycle we were in.

Our family quit eating out on the Sabbath. And yes, over time, as we learned eternal financial principles and the parameters of the "prosperity stick," our family prospered.

As a freshman in college I went to my first day of class, only to realize two-thirds of the way through that I was in the wrong class. I looked around, embarrassed and frustrated. I tried not to bump people as I excused myself quietly from the front and center of the room and finally found the right class, but it was too late; the class was already over. I'd missed the most important day of the semester–the day the teacher explains his syllabus and everything he expects from us that semester.

Once my son was making homemade clam chowder and I told him that the canned milk was in the cupboard. An hour later as our family sat down to dinner we all kept smirking as we tried to figure out what was wrong with the soup. It finally dawned on me that Jacob had used sweetened condensed milk; it, too, was in a can!

I was supposed to meet my husband at the airport at a certain terminal. Three hours later, with crying children and a sore back from carrying all the bags, we finally found each other. The flight had been changed, and so had the terminal.

These experiences have something in common. Though a great effort was made to accomplish something–though there was willpower, action, follow-through, positive attitude and a host of other great things–the desired outcome didn't happen. In each case the proverbial ladder was climbed, only to realize the ladder was leaning against the wrong wall. Much to our chagrin, other more important parts of life can follow the same pattern.

Maybe you and your spouse keep arguing; maybe your daughter's stomach aches keep returning; maybe Social Security keeps looking doomed; maybe terrorists keep attacking; maybe you are being abused; maybe you keep yelling at your kids; maybe.... You can fill in the blank; you know what your "maybe" is.

What does this have to do with math and science? Everything! The purpose for math and science is to make our lives better and to understand the world around us, and it's time to throw out the old technology and bring on the new.

The old technology, the scientific method, can be related to a ladder. A ladder is used for climbing, and climbing may be necessary when we are trying to get from one place to another. The problem is that the scientific method doesn't care which wall it's leaning against.

For a hundred–no, a thousand–wrong walls, there is only one right wall. For a thousand wrong questions there is one right question.

Isaac Newton knew that scientists could and did "endlessly gather facts and amass observations without productive results."[xviii] Don't climb a ladder that's on the wrong wall. It just wastes time.

We don't have the luxury of wasting time. There comes a time in history when time is critical, and that time is NOW. We need to use the new technology so that we are climbing the right walls and having the outcomes we desire. The scientific method, the old way of doing science, follows this pattern:

1. Observe some aspect of the universe.
2. Invent a tentative description, called a hypothesis, which is consistent with what you have observed.
3. Use the hypothesis to make predictions.
4. Test those predictions by experiments or further observations and modify the hypothesis in the light of your results.
5. Repeat steps 3 and 4 until there are no discrepancies between theory and experiment and/or observation.

The scientific method makes no distinction between important observation and superfluous observation, between being on the right wall or the wrong wall.

When I was fifteen and overheard my parents' conversation, I don't know what they planned to do–what hypothesis they came up with–to solve the problem. I do know that when my husband and I run into a roadblock we look at it very carefully so as not to be deceived as we try to determine what can really solve it.

I call using the scientific method the "antibiotic" approach. I'm sure many of you have taken your child to the doctor only to have what you already knew confirmed: "Yes, your child has an earache and it is infected. Here's your antibiotic."

I had a friend whose child went through twelve rounds of antibiotics in eight months for the same recurring problem. I don't know if my friend ever thought to ask, "What is causing the ear infections?" but in this case, the doctor didn't. He treated the symptom, and the symptom kept coming back. He treated the symptom again, and again, and again, and again.

This is a trap that's all too easy to fall into. Applying the Inteligro Method™ can get us out. Here is the new technology, the way to get to the root of the problem and solve it.

This is an exercise, so be sure to have your pencil ready.

Step 1. Notice a Problem or Roadblock

Let's use a real example. My husband is a scientist, and he used to manufacture a science kit with a sea monkey-type shrimp called a "triops." His buyer asked him to kill off all the bacteria in the kit in order to make the triops safe for children. Rick, my husband, found that if he killed all the bacteria, the triops would hatch but die shortly thereafter. In other words, either the triops lived on the bacteria or the method used to kill the bacteria also killed the food. This was a problem.

Now write down a problem you have noticed:

____

____

____

____

____

Step 2. The Heart: Be Interested—Care Enough to Have Initiative

My husband cared a lot about the fact that the triops died if he killed off the bacteria. Our income depended on his solving the problem. The safety of children buying the science kits depended on him solving the problem. So he cared a lot about solving this problem.

How much do you care about the problem you wrote down in step one? If you don't care that much about it but should, then start caring. Or, if you wrote down a problem that's no big deal, erase it and own up to something real. This exercise can change your life if you let it. I want you to pick a problem that you care about—on a scale of 1-10—at level ten!

Once you have written down a problem that you care deeply about, move on.

Step 3. Use Spiritual Eyes to Name the Real Problem

a. People with spiritual eyes have trained their eyes to see what others miss
b. Notice patterns
c. Notice symptoms of problem
d. Ask, "What is the cause or real problem?"
e. Listen, ponder, think, meditate - follow instincts and hunches
f. Identify the glitch, the bottleneck, or real problem
g. Name the problem and arrange it in the form of "the right question"

Step three takes a lot of effort; we are going to go through each step.

a. People with spiritual eyes have trained their eyes to see what others miss.
Was my husband missing something? What were the patterns? He noticed how the triops lived with the bacteria versus without and started jotting down all the data.

b. Notice patterns.
The patterns included: when he didn't kill the bacteria, the captive triops could grow to two inches in length in the right habitat. When he did kill the bacteria, the captive triops hatched and then died within 48 hours, barely becoming visible to the naked eye.

c. Notice symptoms of problem.
The symptom was that the triops would die when the bacteria was removed. The symptoms also included the fact that when

the bacteria remained it was unsafe for humans.

d. Ask, "What is the cause or real problem?"
What is the real problem? Was the problem that the bacteria were unsafe for humans? Was the problem that the triops needed the bacteria? Was the problem the fact that when the bacteria were killed the triops died? Was the method used for killing the bacteria also harming the triops' eggs?

e. Listen, ponder, think, meditate - follow instincts and hunches.
My husband brainstormed many possible scenarios. He pondered, thought, listened, and followed his hunch. His hunch was that the triops fed on the bacteria. He was killing their food, and so they could not survive.

f. Identify the glitch, bottleneck, or real problem.
Therefore, the real problem was that he needed to find a food that fed the triops and was also safe for humans to handle.

g. Name the problem and arrange it in the form of "the right question."
The right question then was, "What can the triops eat that is safe for humans to be around?"

Now let's go through the same steps with your problem.

a. People with spiritual eyes have trained their eyes to see what others miss.
Are you seeing everything? Remember Thales? His workers ignored some of the evidence, but he didn't. He took it all in and saw the obvious: the salt dissolved when the donkey lay in the water. Are you noticing everything? The following steps can help you notice more.

b. Notice patterns.
What are the patterns surrounding your problem? What

have you noticed? This is a very important step; don't skip it. Write them all down. Write down everything that comes to your mind over the next sixty seconds:

____

____

____

____

____

____

____

c. Notice symptoms of problem.

Often when we name a problem for the first time we are really only naming the symptom. An earache is a symptom of an ear infection. An ear infection can be a symptom of a poor diet; bacteria; a virus; overall poor health due to allergens; clogged lymph, digestive, lung and skin systems, etc.

Look at your problem and see if you actually named a symptom of the real thing. Start naming all the symptoms surrounding the problem and see if you have actually only named one of the symptoms. Naming many of the symptoms—or the "...then this" part of the "if this...then this" equation—can help identify the "if this..." portion. Brainstorm more of the symptoms:

____

____

____

____

____

____

d. Ask, "What is the cause or real problem?"

Now, after naming more symptoms, ask, "What is the cause or real problem?" Maybe you hit it on the head the first try, maybe not. Here's where you identify the cause if you didn't already.

____
____
____
____

e. Listen, ponder, think, meditate - follow instincts and hunches.

What is your hunch? What do your instincts tell you the real problem might be? If you need to ponder about this while you do the dishes, go ahead. Or if you need to set down the book and meditate, feel free. Listen to the thoughts in your heart and mind. What do you hear? What do you see? What do you feel? What do you know?

____
____
____
____
____
____

f. Identify the glitch, the bottleneck, or real problem.

What is the real problem? Write it down. Don't be afraid to follow your hunch and instinct.

____
____
____
____

g. Name the problem and arrange it in the form of "the right question."

This part is very important. Remember Newton? Discovering and clarifying the right question leads you to the direct path of finding the answer. Word your question for solving the problem carefully. What is your "right question"? This is akin to climbing the right wall. This is the crux of the difference between the old technology and the new. The new technology, The Inteligro Method,™ assumes that there is a hierarchy of questions, and that there is a right question to ask. So figure out the right question.

____

____

____

____

____

Step 4. Ask the Right Question.

Once my husband figured out the right question, he asked it. He asked it on paper, out loud, to me, to our three year old, to the triops and to the Universe. He put it out there, and he expected an answer.

Ask your right question!

____

____

____

____

____

Step 5. Spiritual Creation: brainstorm options that might solve the problem.

I have chills going down my spine and arms to my finger tips just thinking about Step 5. I love Step 5. My friends will tell you that my favorite thing to do is ask the right question and then study "that stick." Remember the "prosperity stick" I began studying when I was fifteen? I found some of the laws of the Universe—some of the truths that, if I held onto them, would produce certain results. Remember I found that keeping the Sabbath Day holy directly impacted our prosperity?

This step is the really fun part. This is where you get to apply the first two Inteligros in a clear and focused way: you search out the truth, you find out everything you can about your proverbial stick (now that you've named it) and you use logic to follow choices to their clear end.

Everything has two creations, not just the earth. The creation of the earth shows us the pattern of all creation—a spiritual creation followed by a physical creation. Step 5 is where you spiritually create. It happens in your brain first, then in reality. Nobody has ever done anything without having thunk it first. (I know—"thunk" isn't a word, but I like it and use it.)

My husband filled pages of a notebook while brainstorming answers to his right question. His question was, "What can the triops eat that is safe for humans to be around?"

It took my husband six months, working full time, before he found a suitable food. He filled his notebook with ideas he could try. He realistically thought about some of them and scratched them out because they potentially created the same bacteria dilemma. He finally had several options to pick from after a couple of weeks of brainstorming and studying all he could about triops and other creatures like them and what they ate. He studied at the library and on the internet. He studied everything he could get into his hands. He went to the sites where he gathered the triops and compared the various habitats.

He was virtually on the cutting edge of biology. I've told him for years that he should have published his findings, for he was asking a question no other biologist had ever asked, at least as far as he could research.

What do you know about your subject, your "stick"? At first your brainstorm might simply lead you to where you need to study. This step should take some time. If you have named a problem, it probably didn't get there overnight, and it probably won't go away overnight. You might need to dedicate some real time to learning all you can about your topic.

This is why Step 2 is so important. There's no way you would put in the necessary time if you didn't care. The heart—your heart—is a big indicator of whether or not you will see this through.

You are trying to discover the truth about your topic. For example, when Great Britain taxed her American colonies and wouldn't redress their grievances, the colonies eventually broke away and won their freedom. The colonists were then faced with a major problem: how to govern themselves and maintain their hard-earned freedom and liberty.

Do you know how long the greatest men and women studied that question? Do you know how many books were consulted? How many prayers were offered? How many lives were given? How many debates argued? How many papers written? How much money spent? How much effort it took to find all they could about governing themselves?

They studied the Romans, the Greeks, the Anglo Saxons, the French, the Germans and the English. They consulted the *Bible*, Plato, Aristotle, Socrates, Cicero, Montesquieu and countless others. They sacrificed personal businesses to serve, left families and traveled to distant countries. They worked *really hard* to find the natural laws—the self-evident and revealed laws—concerning the governance of a commonwealth, to figure out their options and to choose the best, right one.

So if your task looks daunting, "gird up your loins and fresh courage take."

Your prize is only worth your work. For now, write down everything you know about your topic. Let me give you an example of the "prosperity stick" I have filled out over the years. This diagram is the first level of my brainstorm. I've made a quick sketch. Each outer point has its own further brainstorms.

After my original brainstorming, I then take each line to its

full length of reasoning. These are the lines of logic I use to discover what is true. I take each one of those outer points, think of what each one means and write the consequence of using it.

For instance, under the one called "Sabbath Day" I discover what it means to keep the Sabbath Day holy, and then I write the consequences for doing it. If you remember, that day when I was fifteen, I found that there were several natural consequences for keeping the Sabbath Day holy, some of which included:

- a fullness of the earth
- the herb
- good things, whether for food or raiment, or houses, or barns, or orchards, or gardens or vineyards
- things to please the eye and gladden the heart; for taste, for smell to strengthen the body and to enliven the soul. [xix]

I do this for each brainstormed point. Under "Wealth" I discovered it links to "capital" and "labor" and "natural resources." I found that wealth comes from the ability to turn natural resources and capitol into something useful or beautiful that benefits mankind. Brigham Young, the leader who settled parts of the West, said two interesting things about wealth. One was that after spending a relatively short time with a wife, he could tell whether or not the husband would be wealthy just by noticing what the woman did with what the man brought in. Was she wasteful? Did she live providently? Could she turn something drab into something beautiful? By the same token, did the two together have the ability to turn a stump into a chair? Turn dirt into a garden? Turn wool into a dress? Turn paint into a picture? If so, there was wealth.

Now it's your turn.

Write your brainstorm and spend some time on it. When you are finished invite a colleague, friend, sister, spouse or child to help you brainstorm some more. Think-tanks are great at this point. Often someone else knows something we don't. Don't forget to consult great literature on the topic.

Once you can see the laws surrounding your dilemma it's time to make a choice.

Step 6. Choose the best, right option.

Choose the one you think is the best, right option. Let me console you up front. You may make the wrong choice. So what? That's what life is about: learning. Choose it and move forward. The sooner you act on it, the sooner you'll know whether it works. So let's get started. Remember to trust the process of discovery.

Step 7. Physical creation: Create a system to implement the option.

It is now time for the physical creation. You need to have planned a system so that your option can be implemented. In other words, once my husband realized there was no known food for the triops other than whatever it was they ate in their natural habitat, he knew he had to test "stuff" that was safe for humans. His chosen system was to buy twenty to forty items a week at the health food store and set up tests at home to see if they worked.

He had control groups and tested four different amounts for each food item.

So, what is your system? Plan it out and write it below:

____

____

____

____

____

____

____

____

____

____

____

____

____

____

____

Step 8. Implement.

Now go do it.

Like I said, my husband's implementation was a six-month process. He tested hundreds of foods before he found one suitable for both humans and triops.

Step 9. Evaluate implementation.

What were your results? Did it work?

Step 10. Make necessary adjustments or changes (cycles back to Step 5 - Spiritual Creation).

Every Sunday night my husband and I have what we call our Executive Council meeting, or our Family Executive Council meeting (F.E.C.). We are the executives of our family, and we meet together to evaluate whether our family is functioning the way we want it to.

Every Sunday we ask ourselves how we are doing. This is an on-going process. We discuss our children, our finances and ourselves. We discuss our goals, commitments and missions. We even discuss the dog. We don't discuss everything every time, but everything gets discussed. We make adjustments when necessary, we laugh, we cry, we solve problems. This is real science. What greater contribution to society is there than well-raised children?

We take notes. We keep track of improvements, digressions and crimes committed–like messes left, too much teasing and coats left on the floor. We discuss new ways to get eight-year-old Joseph to read, to get five-year-old Melanie to go to bed at night or to find more time for mom to write. We take statistics, we take measurements, we analyze data and we manipulate materials. This is real math, and we love doing it. Creating a family unit that aligns itself with eternal laws and lives by them takes weekly and daily adjustments. Solving your dilemma will take this much effort as well.

Don't be discouraged by Step 10. Make necessary adjustments, cycle back to the spiritual creation, visualize options and follow their line of logic, seeing them through to their clear ends. Pick your next step, create your system and implement it.

When my husband first started testing foods he had no idea it would take six months to find something the triops could live on. He had to go back again and again to the health food store and buy hundreds of different items–from wheat grass and fructose to acidophilus and wheat germ and so on–until he finally found what he now calls "Number 28." It's top secret, and he's sworn me to secrecy. I am allowed to reveal the triops food to no one. Until, of course, someone needs it.

The point is that science takes time. The Inteligro Method™ works. It works in behavioral science, in political science, in medical science and in social science. It is science.

Our next right question is: how can we apply Inteligro math in our homes with our children? This will be the venue of our next chapter.

Chapter 6

INTELIGRO MATH

AGES 1 TO 18

"Mom, I've got a really good one!" my eight-year old son said with his eyes lit up as he gave me another riddle. "Would you rather be...allergic to your mom, or your dog?"

Now I knew he was teasing me. It's not because he is a perpetual tease that I caught on (though he is). It's because I'm allergic to dogs, and our dog is his best friend. To him the question is a rather devastating one. He would really hate to be allergic to the dog, almost as much as if he were allergic to me.

I reached across the table and messed up his hair, "I'd rather be allergic to you, so you just keep petting Lady, okay?"

Joseph laughed his mirthful laugh and continued playing cards with me. We were doing our weekly ritual of playing math games. I like playing "war" with our fraction cards. I still need the cheat sheet, but the kids just about know whether 2/3 is greater than 5/6 or whether 7/10 is less than ¼ without the hands-on manipulative.

Inteligro Math is such a new approach to math and science that I'm inevitably asked, "But how do I do it with my children?" This chapter contains tips for making your child's mathematics study as much about truth, logic and the characteristics of a scientist as it is about numbers and formulas.

As a reminder, the four Inteligros we will be teaching our children are:

1) Seek after and recognize truth.

2) Learn to think things through, reason things out, and follow a line of logic.

3) Develop the habits of a scientist, especially the vital ones.

4) Gain Newtonian math skills—master the language and measurement of math and science.

And of course, we will use the Inteligro Method™ to solve problems.

1. "Truth-speak."

The first eight years of a child's life are the perfect time to teach a child the difference between truth and lies. They learn at a young age to see cause and effect. If we don't lie to ourselves it will be much easier to teach this to them.

Though a two year old might be ten feet away from you when she trips and comes up saying, "you did that to me," she learns very quickly whether you mean it when you say, "Climb back in bed or you'll get a spanking."

During the child's core phase of their education, when they are building the foundation of what is right and what is wrong, what is true and what is not, what is good and what is bad,[xx] we must remember to "truth-speak" and to be consistent.

Gandhi is a perfect example of truth-speaking. Satygraha is one form of truth-speaking, or truth-living. The more we align our lives with what we known is true and right, the more we truth-speak. A good way to measure your truth-speaking is to honestly answer the following questions: "Do you deceive anyone? Are any of your communications deceiving anyone?" I remember when I looked at those questions and answered them squarely. I was surprised to see that there were two instances in which my communication was deceptive. It took some work, but I cleared it up. I began to be more like Gandhi and truth-speak.

2. Read to your family from your core book.

No matter their ages, read to your children daily from your core book. This is one place you find your truth, so set the example for them. As they get older you can even share the insights and equations you find as well as the lines of logic you have followed. They like this, and in turn will share their insights with you. Watch out, for they often see more clearly than we do.

3. Set up environments that develop the vital habits of a scientist.

The characteristics of a scientist are found naturally and intrinsically in children. We simply need to encourage, rather than squelch, the development of noticing patterns, exploring the world, wondering why things are the way they are, testing ideas, caring about life outside themselves and stick-to-itiveness.

Children need free time. As parents, we sometimes overcrowd our children's schedules. Isaac Newton was able to explore the world around him for days on end. We need to give some of that freedom to our children. They need time in which they are free to explore, when we are not telling them what to do. It helps if they don't have any destructive addictions like video gaming and television watching. These will kill a child's initiative as fast as fats, salts, and sugars kill a man's heart. Time-wasting television shows and video gaming are not even an option in many of the homes where Inteligro Math is taught.

Time is one of our most valuable commodities, and we should frown upon time-stealers. Why in the world would a child do something hard–like thinking–if they can be numbed by a video game?

If you home-school you can offer classes in any scientific field to the local home-schoolers and make it fun. Create environments that develop the habits of a scientist. When these are developed, the Newtonian skills will follow.

Focus on creating a learning environment that develops a certain trait, such as noticing patterns, or encourages the students to "wonder." Help them follow their hearts and learn to care about projects and problems. The vital characteristics are named for you in Chapter 3. Create an environment that develops these in your children.

For example, let's say you want to inspire your children to develop the habit of seeing patterns. You would start by asking yourself, "What kind of environment can I create which will inspire my children and teach them to notice patterns?"

The next thing you would do is take out a piece of paper and brainstorm for two minutes. Write down everything that comes to mind. Maybe you wrote down some great manipulatives you have that can be put into patterns. Maybe you wrote down the idea of going on a nature walk and pointing out patterns that occur in nature, such as those found in rocks, trees, clouds, plants, etc. Maybe you wrote down the idea to read The Little House on the Prairie series with your children and point out patterns you notice as you read. Maybe you wrote down some projects that require pattern recognition, like doing a sewing project, building something out of wood or learning to draw together.

The point is, after you have brainstormed the options, pick the best, right one that suits your family and your needs and implement it.

4. Let your children own and solve their problems.

A good way to incorporate the Inteligro Method™ is to allow your children to take responsibility for their own choices and to solve problems, alone and together.

My nine-year-old daughter is rather good at naming problems. "Mom, Melanie's friends used all my make-up again and left the dress-ups all over my room!"

My response depends on her voice. We don't allow any "Whiny-baby-booby-buts" (a term my sister coined) at our house. Laura learned this very quickly.

"Laura, are you coming to complain and whine to me? Or do you want to solve the problem?"

She would usually have to gain control over her emotions at that point, and then I would say, "When you want to solve the problem come talk to me. If you just want to complain, do it somewhere else or calm down and come get a hug."

She'd sober up real quick and say, "I want to solve the problem."

"Great. What do you recommend?"

"No more five year olds in my room!"

"That won't work. It's her room, too. What else?"

We'd work on it, brainstorm it, and figure out that the make-up shouldn't be kept where five year olds can reach it, that perhaps we need to find a different place for Melanie and her friends to play, that maybe we should have clean-up time before friends leave, and that Mom will definitely talk to Melanie about not getting into other people's things.

Now when Laura comes to me she tells me the problem and three possible solutions to it. She learns quickly.

5. Use helps—don't reinvent the wheel.

For Newtonian math—measurement and math language skills—I highly recommend using products by Joan Cotter. I like having her products for game playing and for young children (twelve and younger) to use on their own initiative. She has studied Asian culture and compared it to American culture and has shown that the math and science taught in American schools is leading to a rapid decline of mathematicians and scientists. She has a seminar that she presents, and her website can be found on the internet by doing a search on her name. Honestly, she taught me better ways to teach my children. I highly recommend buying her game set and instruction book and playing games with your children using her math manipulatives.

For older students, my friends recommend a wonderful set of videos called Videotext. They love the way Newtonian math is taught in these videos.

You must realize that the world will put pressure on you to judge only the Newtonian skills of your children, but that Newtonian skills are just one of the Inteligros. Newtonian math is simply the expression of the other three Inteligros. Please don't put undue pressure on yourself "not to leave your child behind." Do yourself, and them, a huge favor by using the Inteligro Portfolio to help you stay focused on the fact that math and science are about finding truths and applying those truths in your life.

For children under the age of eight, use manipulatives and lots of games. Set aside a time or two each week to do puzzles, play games, clap out rhythms, learn nursery rhymes, etc. Joan Cotter's games teach the concepts in a fun and comprehensive way.

For the Apprentice Scholar student (usually age fourteen and up), use The Pyramid Project™–the Scholar Project I designed using the four Inteligros. This Scholar Project is taught once a week over the course of the year and jump-starts students into using the four Inteligros and the Inteligro Method.™ **If you would like to know more about The Pyramid Project™, go to www.lemiinstitute.com or www.inteligromath.com**

By the time a child is fourteen, we want them to have surpassed what the state standardized testing, the lowest denominator, says is healthy. We want them to be ready for Inteligro math as they enter Scholar Phase. This means they will be doing math the Inteligro way for a minimum of one to two hours a day. They read original math and science classics, do original research using the Inteligro Method, ™ learn Newto-nian math (as well as figuring out new procedures), develop a keen sense of logic, and search for and apply truth in their lives.

6. Play musical instruments.

For students over eight, I highly recommend a musical instrument. Read Shinichi Suzuki's book, "Nurtured by Love", and enroll in musical lessons yourself. Please realize that the day your child turns eight I don't expect you to march to the phone book and hire a piano teacher. In your Family Executive Council meetings with your spouse, discuss items like this and find the right timing.

As I mentioned before, in the last six months our family has begun music lessons. My twelve year old, my nine year old, my eight year old, and I have been taking piano lessons. My five year old and my 8-month-old baby are seeing our examples and, I expect, will eventually follow suit.

7. Be picky.

Choose your children's teachers well. Be picky. Don't just let your child's lot be chosen for them. One of the best gifts my parents gave me was their fight for my right to have the best teachers.

Not all teachers are equal. You know this. You went to school, and usually you can tell which teachers are good. They are the ones who inspire your children to want to learn. Give your children the best teachers, and be an inspiring teacher yourself.

8. Use the Inteligro Portfolio.

The Inteligro Portfolio is designed to do three things.

1. Inspire you to *do* Inteligro Math. The pages within the Portfolio inspire you to study in your core book daily, to annotate math and science classics, to experiment, to be curious, to notice patterns, and to find alternative procedures for known math algorithms. Each record sheet inspires you to self-educate.

2. Act as a measuring device. The biggest measuring device in current schools emphasizes Newtonian math skills. It does not measure your ability to sift through gobs of information to find the relevant, your ability to recognize and use patterns, or your ability to create other alternatives for getting something done. The Inteligro Portfolio is a self-measuring tool to help you know how well you apply all four Inteligros.

3. Keep a record. Scientists keep records of their findings, and so should we. Having a record of all the math classics you annotate may come in handy one day. Having a record of the science experiments and projects you engage in may change someone's life one day. Keeping a record of the things you are curious about may one day reveal something important. Keeping track of the patterns you comprehend could lead to new discoveries. Your portfolio is a journal of your search for and application of truth.

9. Use Groups.

Any number more than one is a group. Yes, figuring out the world around us takes place in the brain, but groups can help spark thought. Lavoisier worked with his wife who would read mathematicians' texts, translate them, and give Lavoisier a condensed version so that he could learn the meat of it and move on. He and his wife made a great group. He also worked with a team as they drew up the table of elements, eventually condensing long sentences into one-letter terms.

Isaac Newton published *Philosophiae Naturalis Principa Mathematica* only with the help of his assistant, Humphrey Newton, who helped translate for him and get the book ready for publication.

I encourage my young scholar students to study regularly in groups—once a month at least. Once a week is even better. They have more fun coming up with alternative procedures for Newtonian math, and they love doing experiments together. The ideas they share with each other generate more ideas, and the growing enthusiasm leads to incredible new knowledge and discoveries.

10. Projects, Projects, Projects.

As I mentioned previously, a highly specialized person who has taken their course of study to the microscopic "parts" is in a state of bondage. That is, if they started in the "parts," not the "whole," or never moved to the whole. Inteligro math invites the study of the world at large on a "whole" level. All four Inteligros are used in order to do math and science. TRUTH is sought after, REASONING and LOGIC are employed to discern it, the HABITS of a SCIENTIST practiced, and NEWTONIAN language is used to measure, quantify, qualify and communicate the discovery.

Projects are the answer. When you do projects with your children and students all four Inteligros are used. Math and science is discovered from a whole to parts to whole progression.

Take a watch for instance. Imagine an eight year old taking

the watch apart and setting each cog, wheel, pin and magnet, each separate piece, carefully on the table. After he has the entire watch taken apart, imagine him picking up each part, one at a time, and carefully studying it. He picks up a part with the tweezers, drops it in his other hand, feels it, looks closely at it and squeezes it. He might even bite it with his teeth (remember, this is an uninhibited eight year old we are talking about here). He remembers how the piece looked inside the watch and tries to fit it to the other pieces for a moment. Then he finally sets it down and moves to the next piece. He studies that part in the same manner he studied the first one, always keeping in mind that this is part of the watch—one piece of the puzzle. It is part of what makes a watch a watch. Sure, it can stand alone, for he is holding it alone in his hands, but when put together in the right way, with the right tools, it turns into something completely different. This element becomes part of the whole. It becomes a new creature altogether. Its function is utilized.

Studying through projects is very much like the watch analogy. Through projects, each piece is put in its rightful place. Truth is self-evident, logic is used, patterns and judgments are made, and the use of numbers and measurements is obvious.

Great math and science projects are done holistically. Some include sewing, baking, learning a musical instrument, woodworking, developing artistic talent, gardening and animal husbandry.

Any and all of these projects are wonderful holistic math and science. Each uses all four Inteligros. A child doesn't ask, "When will I ever use fractions?" if they bake regularly. A child doesn't need to be told how important measurements are if they design and build things out of wood or sew fabric. A child doesn't get frustrated by multiplication facts if he has a quarter of an acre planted with corn, beans, peas and squash. Calculating begins to come naturally, and the happy realization of the times tables memorized is felt or desired.

Projects are the answer when it comes to doing Inteligro Math in your home.

11. Use simulations.

Smack! I hoped that the slap from my niece's hand across her brother's face sounded worse than it felt. I watched my sister take her daughter aside.

"Sweetheart," she said as she knelt down and looked straight into her little girl's eyes, "we don't solve our problems by hitting. Now why don't you tell me what's going on?"

The little one proceeded to tell Mommy that she wanted her toy and Brother wouldn't give it back to her. Thus, the slap.

"What else could you do to get your toy back?"

This question caused my niece to furrow her brow. Thinking isn't always easy. Finally she thought of and suggested something.

"Yes, that would work. What else would work?"

This went on for a few minutes and then Mommy said, "Which of these ways is best?"

Once they decided which course of action was the right one, Mommy then did something incredible. She simulated the event with her daughter, helping her create and cement the pathway in her mind, making her more likely to follow the new pathway the next time.

"Sweetheart, let's pretend that Brother has your toy and you want it back. I'm Brother and I have your toy. What should you do?" she said, reaching for one of the toys.

My niece proceeded to re-enact the best, right choice.

How and why is this math and science? My sister was teaching her daughter the art of problem solving. There was more than one choice when it came to getting the toy back. My little three year old niece was learning that hitting wasn't her only and best option and that getting angry didn't help.

For children under the age of eight, simulations like this are critical. We simulate anything and everything in our home: how to respond when mom or dad asks you to do something, what to do when the goats get out and how to hang up your coat when you come inside the house on a blustery day. Simulations are another name for "teaching."

A child under the age of eight often doesn't know the difference between reality and fantasy. Little Polly Pocket figures and Lego men are as real to them as our friends are to us. How else could your six year old spend hour after hour with these playthings? Their world is a world of discovery. And all they need is the gift of time so that they can discover.

At this young age boundaries are learned–such as not hitting, taking care of toys and not sassing. Boundaries have everything to do with math and science, for boundaries make good little boys and girls.

As children get older, more simulations can be utilized. It is fun to take clay, Popsicle sticks, newspapers, or any such object, and challenge the children to build the strongest bridge they can. Crushing the bridges is just as fun as building them. This simulation can then lead to the study of bridge building, which utilizes an incredible amount of math and science.

Implement simulations in your math and science and you will be doing Inteligro math.

12. Speak the language!

Doing Inteligro math can be as easy as simply speaking the language. When we are driving in a blizzard and notice seven cars have slid off the road, we can comment to our children, "I've noticed a peculiar pattern this evening as we drive home in this blizzard. Has anyone else noticed it?"

"Yeah, I did. The snowflakes coming down are obscuring our vision, and when you turn on your bright lights it gets worse."

"Wow, its true. Anyone else notice a pattern?"

"I did. You make us be quiet when you drive in bad weather."

"Hmm, I never noticed that one. Thanks for pointing it out. Any others?"

"Yes, there are several cars off the road."

"Why do you suppose that is?"

"Maybe their kids didn't be quiet."

After a few sighs one child says, "I suppose it's because they hydroplaned on the slush or because they were going too fast."

Or maybe you are working in your garden together one day when your nine year old asks, "How many peas do you think we'll grow this year, Mom?"

"Well, let's measure it. Let's use our Newtonian math skills to figure it out. What will it take to figure it out?"

"Hmm, we need to know how many seeds we planted and guess how many pods will be on each plant."

"Yes. Do we want to go back and count each seedling, or shall we do some adding and multiplying?"

Then, of course, the row can be measured. Since you planted a pea seedling every inch, and there are fifteen feet in each row, and you planted six rows, how many plants were planted? Based on the last three years of gardening, does each seedling actually grow or do you get about a 70% success rate? And finally, after you've figured out how many plants will grow, you need to figure out how many pea pods grow on each plant and the average number of peas in each pod. Our biggest pod has eight or nine peas per pod, but some pods only have four or five.

Can you see the math? All it takes is a little language to help your child realize they are using Newtonian math to measure, quantify, qualify and communicate. In the end the nine year old knows that there will be enough peas for daily consumption for three weeks for the whole family, plus enough to give away to friends and neighbors and maybe even twelve quarts for the freezer.

A little language goes a long way.

Or you may have a child who is trying to get out of doing the dishes on Friday night by using logic. "I know it's my turn on Friday, but last week when it was Little Sister's turn I did the dishes for her because she was sick. So it stands to reason, Mom, that you should make her take my turn on Friday."

"I can see you are good at using logic to reason this out. You missed the point though, son. You gave freely to your sister when you did the dishes for her. I can't make her do your job; that would go against our family values. Is there another way?"

"Well, when you put it like that I can see that I ought to convince her to do the dishes for me."

"Yes, that would be the better logic."

Use the language of math and science and your children will grow up doing math and science. Talk about patterns, show the line of logic as you read to your children, point out truths as you live, teach the difference between solving just any problem and boiling it down to the right problem, enjoy wondering about the world together. Show your children how fun it is to measure, quantify and qualify. And use that language.

13. Trust yourself and enjoy Inteligro Math™!

You are the steward over your home; so if your next best, right question is, "How do I do this in my home?" apply the Inteligro Method.™ Don't cheat yourself out of the opportunity to solve your own problem. Trust yourself and enjoy the journey with your children.

In this chapter I have given you a few tips and ideas for applying Inteligro Math in your home. You are the steward of your home. You know what is needed. You know which Inteligro to focus on, and you can create an environment and project that not only captures it, but also uses all four Inteligros. So trust yourself and have fun.

Appendix: Chart of Inteligro Method™

Old	New
The Scientific Method	**The Inteligro Method™**
1. Observe some aspect of the universe.	1. Notice a problem or roadblock.
2. Invent a tentative description, called a hypothesis, that is consistent with what you have observed.	2. The heart–be interested, care enough to have initiative.
3. Use the hypothesis to make predictions.	3. Use spiritual eyes to name the real problem. a. People with spiritual eyes have trained their eyes to see what others miss. b. Notice patterns. c. Notice symptoms of problem. d. Ask, "What is the cause or real problem?" e. Listen, ponder, think, meditate - follow instincts and hunches. f. Identify the glitch, the bottleneck, or real problem. g. Name the problem and arrange it in the form of "the right question."
4. Test those predictions by experiments or further observations and modify the hypothesis in the light of your results.	4. Ask the right question.
5. Repeat Steps 3 and 4 until there are no discrepancies between theory and experiment and/or observation.	5. Spiritual Creation: brainstorm options that might solve problem. (Line of Logic)
	6. Choose the best, right option.
	7. Physical Creation: create a system to implement the right option.
	8. Implement.
	9. Re-evaluate implementation.
	10. Make necessary adjustments or changes, cycles back to Step 5 - Spiritual Creation.

End Notes

[i]Oliver DeMille, 2000. A *Thomas Jefferson Education*. Utah: George Wythe College Press.

[ii]Lynn and Gray Poole, 1962. *Scientists Who Changed the World. New York*: Dodd, Mead & Company, p. 153.

[iii]Noah Webster, 1828. *American Dictionary of the English language.*

[iv]Bryce D. Gibby, 2003. *Valiant Young Women.* Perlycross Publishers, p. 29.

[v]Lynn and Gray Poole, 1962. *Scientists Who Changed the World*. New York: Dodd, Mead & Company, p. 76.

[vi] Ibid. 62.

[vii] C.S. Lewis, 1994. *The Inspirational Writings of C.S. Lewis*. Inspirational Press, p 75-76.

[viii] Lynn and Gray Poole, 1962. *Scientists Who Changed the World*. New York: Dodd, Mead & Company, p. 47.

[ix] Joan Cotter, seminar on mathematics in America.

[x] Ibid. 147.

[xi] Louis Agassiz 1874, *Evolution and fermanence of Type.* Published posthumously by The *Allantic Monthly*

[xii] Albret einstein, 1961. *Realativity*. New York: Random House. P 10

[xiii] Henri Poincare. *Science and Method*. New York: Dover Publications. P. 15

[xiv] Archimedes. *The Sand Reckoner*

[xv] Oliver DeMille frequently teaches "You are each a genius."

[xi] Doctrine and Covenants 82:10.

[xii] Doctrine and Covenants 59:16-19.

[xiii] Lynn and Gray Poole, 1962. *Scientists Who Changed the World*. New ork: Dodd, Mead & Company, p. 46.

[xiv] Doctrine and Covenants 59:16-19.

[xv] Oliver and Rachel DeMille, 2004. *Core and Love of Learning.*

About the author:

Tiffany Rhoades Earl is the mother of five children and married to Richard Dean Earl. She is the President of Leadership Education Mentoring Institute, which develops scholar projects and trains teachers in the leadership model. She is the co-author of The Thomas Jefferson Planner with Oliver DeMille. Tiffany has a B.A. in Biblical Studies and a M.A. in Education. She and her husband home-school their five children and reside in Blackfoot, Idaho.

Other publications by Tiffany Earl, either published or soon to be, include:

- The New Commonwealth School. With Aneladee Milne
- The Thomas Jefferson Planner. With Oliver DeMille
- The Mentor. With Oliver DeMille
- The Inteligro Portfolio
- The Pyramid Project
- The Thomas Jefferson Youth Certification

Questions or comments regarding these publications or seminars by Tiffany Earl may be sent to Leadership Education Mentoring Institute Press at tiffany@lemiinstitute.com